Up on the Roof
New and Selected Poems

MATTHEW SWEENEY

Up on the Roof
New and Selected Poems

illustrated by
DAVID AUSTEN

*To Jade and Amber,
Best wishes,
Matthew Sweeney*

faber and faber

faber and faber

First published in 2001
by Faber and Faber Limited
3 Queen Square London WC1N 3AU

Photoset by Wilmaset Ltd., Birkenhead, Wirral

Printed in England by
Mackays of Chatham plc, Chatham, Kent

ISBN 0–571–20728–6

ACKNOWLEDGEMENTS
'The Tunnel' from *A Smell of Fish* (Jonathan Cape, 2000)
and 'The House' from *The Bridal Suite* (Jonathan Cape, 1997)
are reprinted by kind permission of the Random House Group Ltd.
'I Went to the Future' was commissioned by the Barbican as part
of their *Dreamspaces* educational project in 2000.

2 4 6 8 10 9 7 5 3 1

Contents

A Boy

Half a mile from the sea,
in a house with a dozen bedrooms
he grew up. Who was he?
Oh, nobody much. A boy
with the usual likes
and more than a few dislikes.
Did he swim much? Nah,
that sea was the Atlantic
and out there is *Ice*land.
He kept his play inland
on an L-shaped football pitch
between the garage and the gate.
What did he eat?

Stuff his grandfather made,
home-made sausages,
potted pig's head.
He got the library keys
and carried eight books at a time
home, and he read.
He read so much
he stayed in the book's world.
Wind rattled the window
of his third-storey room,
but his bed was warm.
And he stayed in his bed
half the day if he could,
reading by candlelight
when the storms struck
and the electricity died.
How do I know all this?
You'd guess how if you tried.

Singing Class

There is this image of a tuning-fork
struck against a desk-top to loose
its lone note into a draughty room.
Then the vocal summits of the class

with one boy at least in their midst
dumb for an hour, mouthing air,
the song-words flitting through his head,
his eyes never leaving the inspector.

Cornered

Stand in the corner, John.
Put that dunce's hat on.
Don't even think of turning round –
you're there till home-time, my son,
and longer, if you make a single sound.

What did you do, John?
You know very well, my son.
And stop grinning, the rest of you.
You think this is a piece of fun?
You think I wouldn't swap John for you?

Stop smirking, John.
You're unlike anyone
I've ever met in a classroom.
You're subnormal, my son.
What do you ever do when you're at home?

Don't answer that, John.
And keep the dunce's hat on.
I just might stick it on with glue.
It looks cute on you, my son.
I've plenty stored away for the rest of you.

Off School

As the doctor asked him to,
he rinsed his throat with vinegar
then ate a bag of kumquats.
And soon the bugs had decomposed,
so he banged his bedroom door,
then hurried down the stairs.
Where was he escaping to?
Not school! Great Crikes, the thought!
He was heading for the park, of course,
with his scarf around his neck,
and underneath his jacket
a football. Would he play alone?
You bet! Unless you count the ducks
he curved those corners to,
or the sheep whose heads he found
when he floated free-kicks in,
or the drunk he just persuaded
to sway around in goal.
And what more useful way to spend
a well-earned day off school?

The New Boy

The new boy has many names,
or no name he likes enough to keep.
He comes from Romania, or Austria,
or Hungary, or Albania.
He's a cracker, he's funny, he's a creep.
He has pet bats in his roof garden,
and a pickled dead scorpion,
and he hangs up the skeletons of fish.
He's carving a sarcophagus
out of ebony, and he says
he'll sail in it down the canal.
He likes air balloons, too,
and he wears big-brimmed hats.
Sometimes we're not sure we hear
him right, as his accent's strong,
but seeing as his Dad's the undertaker
we can't be completely wrong.

Blue Hair

In between the dinner ladies
runs the blue-haired boy,
spilling beans and jelly,
and all us kids are yelling
'Catch him! Catch Blue Hair!'
though mostly we like him,
would like to be like him
but wouldn't dare. And look,
he's out front again –
the forks are clattering down –
and haring past our tables,
our laughing, screaming tables,
with five teachers in pursuit
(they'll never catch Blue Hair!).
And none of us can eat,
we're banging with our spoons,
blowing with our breaths,
erupting in a roar
as Blue Hair dodges everyone
and bursts out the door.

Only the Wall

That first day
only the wall saw
the bully
trip the new boy
behind the shed,
and only the wall heard
the name he called,
a name that would stick
like toffee.

The second day
the wall didn't see
the fight
because too many
boys stood around,
but the wall heard
their cheers,
and no one cheered for
the new boy.

The third day
the wall felt
three bullies
lean against it,
ready to ambush
the new boy,
then the wall heard
thumps and cries,
and saw blood.

The fourth day
only the wall missed
the new boy
though five bullies
looked for him,
then picked another boy
instead. Next day
they had him back,
his face hit the wall.

The sixth day
only the wall knew
the bullies
would need that other boy
to savage.
The wall remembered
the new boy's face
going home,
saw he'd stay away.

The Red House

sits in the elm tree
like a nest –
a square, red nest
made of wood.

It would float away if it could.

Its one window
faces north,
the dangerous north.
It has no door –

just a square hole in the floor.

Who lives there?
A monkey,
a red monkey
with no tail –

like a yacht without a sail.

And every evening
a boy,
a blond boy
stands below

to shout into the tree HELLO.

But the monkey
stares down,

scowls down
and won't descend.

He's not the boy's friend.

He was once
when his house,
his red house,
was built.

Now he smells the boy's guilt

that wafts up
to join the pain,
the phantom pain
in his tail.

And the monkey starts to wail

sending the boy
marching home,
running home
like a mouse

while the sun sets on the red house.

Johnjoe's Snowman

Johnjoe built a snowman
shaped like a wigwam
and postbox-sized.

What he didn't tell
was that inside the snowman
he'd stuffed the cat.

All Sunday morning
he patted with his shovel
the sides of that snowman.

He didn't bother with a head.
He'd never seen a snowman
that looked real yet.

How was it a snowman?
Because Johnjoe said so,
and he should know.

When it was finished
he stared at the snowman
and saw it wasn't right.

What the world didn't need
(apart from frozen cats)
was another white snowman.

In memory of the cat
he took the snowman
and sprayed it black.

James's Mum

On the day he was ten years old
James was told
he couldn't keep monkeys any more.
What's a spare bedroom for?
Besides, he only had three.
Was he to set them free?
Who cared if they messed their room?
It wasn't a tomb.
They were living.
James was forgiving
as long as they played with him.
But Mum wanted rid of them,
wanted them on the street,
wanted clean carpet under her feet
in the sitting room,
in the spare bedroom –
anywhere in the house.
She said he could buy a mouse
as long as he bought a cage.
James flew into a rage,
jumped up on the table,
whistled as loud as he was able
till the monkeys hurtled in.
James raised his chin
and pointed at Mum.
Each of the three bit her bum.
Mum ran, screaming, from the house.
'That's what you get for your talk of a mouse!'
James shouted after her,
and there was monkey laughter for
at least an hour.

Then James grew dour
at the thought of Mum's return.
He thought he might burn
the house down.
He realised with a frown
the monkeys had to be gone
when she got home.
Do you want some?
Three, or two, or one?
Hurry up and tell him.
Quickly, here comes Mum.

Honey

The bee buzzed over the honey pot
left open on the table.
'That's mine,' he thought, 'not theirs!
They're as bad as grizzly bears.
I'm going to steal it back if I'm able.'

He hovered and buzzed and dipped
below the rim of the pot
till he could sniff and smell his fill.
It was foreign honey, but still.
Home in the hive there wasn't a lot.

He buzzed in a figure-of-eight
and dodged the sticky spoon.
He flew up and landed on the rim.

How would he get the honey home?
He'd better hurry. They'd be back soon.

Should he go to the hive for help?
Bring a swarm back
to carry each sweet drop at once,
with a dozen bees hanging loose
to guard in case of attack?

He buzzed down to the honey again.
He'd better taste it first.
Who knew what had been done with it?
Boiled, or stuff mixed in with it?
They were known to do their worst.

He landed gently on the meniscus.
He dipped a claw inside
and brought a sticky drop to his mouth.
Six out of ten, he'd tasted worse.
It was time he headed for the hive.

But when he flapped his papery wings
he saw he was stuck there.
He flapped so hard he began to hum.
He telepathized the Queen to come
but he stayed stuck there

till a boy came in and found him,
and pulled his wings off
and squeezed him till he was dead
then spread him, with honey, on bread –
over half a French loaf

which the boy gave to his sister
as they sat down to tea,
and the boy crumbled a bee wing
while the girl swallowed a bee sting.
'Mmn,' she said. 'Wonderful honey!'

My Dear Mungo

My dear Mungo,
it's time you went away –
cleared off to Canada,
there to stay,
up in the tundra
of the frozen North –
Queen Elizabeth Islands
or worse,
where no-one lives
except snowy bears
and long-toothed walruses
and snowier hares –
only up there
could I like you,
send me a snapshot
so I can see you
just as you'll be,
hair past your chin,
a glint in your eye
and ice on your grin,
mouthing your insults
and smart remarks
to leopard seals
and prowling sharks –
my dear Mungo,
head for Heathrow,
I've had it, mate,
beat it, go!

Night Boy

After the cat went out
and the moon sat on the hill
and the sea drowned a lorry
that broke down
                stealing sand,
little, skinny George awoke.

He was little, because he hardly grew.
He hardly grew, because he ate
scraps of chicken, leftover rice, dry bread,
what was left on the dog's plate,
handfuls of cornflakes, jam.
That may sound a lot
but it left George little and skinny.

What about mealtimes? I hear you ask.
Mealtimes, for George, were sleeptimes
most of the year. That's right,
he slept all day,
                got up at night.

What about school? you're saying.
I know, I know what you're like.
What do you know about stars?
Does the sea glow at night
like a green watch-dial?
Ask George, he'll tell you.
He'll even write it down
and read it to you, by torchlight,
and then he'll count the stars.

Blame the holidays, his Gran said,
they're too long.
George lived with his Gran,
George, the sleeper-in
who'd slept in so long, so often,
that now he woke at night
when Gran was asleep.

What did he do at night?
He went to the beach,
lit driftwood fires,
stood in a cave and waited
for spies in submarines
to land.
          He climbed hills
and aeroplane-spotted,
especially small ones
landing in fields.

He hid in ditches
and eavesdropped on strangers.
He woke the neighbour's donkey
and galloped round the field.

25

He lay on a haystack
and watched the dawn.
Then he yawned
                    and went to bed.

And if he met Gran on the stairs,
Good day, was what he said.

The Sleigh

It should have been black
as it hung like a bat upside down
under the stairs, above the rats
that scurried there. Black
would have suited them better,
and would have complemented the snow
that every year or two
brought it into the daylight,
its blue coat faded in blotches
to bare wood, its runners rusty
until we set it on snow
and watched it leave the rust
in streaks behind, then gather
momentum, move freer and freer,
with one of us on it now,
the dog barking alongside.
It never took us long
to remember the best run,
not in a field but on the road
out of town, a steep slope
round a turn that one day
myself, my brother and cousin Kieran
negotiated to find ourselves
heading straight for a lorry,
unable to stop – nothing for it
but go under, which we did,
and my brother, who was on top,
remembers it to this day.

How We Spent Easter

It wasn't a tree-house, more a tree-shed.
It surely wouldn't hold our weight.

Down below, John fed the fire
with driftwood he'd spent weeks collecting.

Kieran boiled the eggs from his uncle's farm
six at a time, in the blackened tin.

Michael stood at the gate, with Spot
primed to growl at the sight of a parent.

Neal juggled the eggcups he'd borrowed,
the spoons jangling in his pockets.

And I was up in the tree-house I'd made,
laying the shaky floor for our feast.

The Tunnel

When they opened the manhole
on the street outside our house
I wanted to climb into it.
I could hear the rats calling.
I could hear the smugglers
manhandling kegs of ale.
I could hear the engine
of a midget U-boat
making inroads from the sea,
and behind it, whispered German,
what these bored submariners
were saying they'd do.
I knew the tunnel went on
down the length of Ireland
and I could row for weeks
in my homemade dingy
before I'd hit the southern coast,
with my strapped-on torch
getting weaker, my water
and sardines running out,
but already I could see
the walls lightening, hear gulls
at the tunnel's end, then the strange
accents of Cork fishermen
who stood and watched me emerge.

The Submerged Door

The bridge by the chocolate shop
arcs like a rainbow whose hues
have drained to a pool of oil
motionless on the black water,
and a boy with a bicycle
dismounts here daily, climbs down
to the canal edge and kneels
peering into the water, moving
his gaze like a torch-beam
until it lights on the door,
and sometimes he reaches
through the oily wet to touch it,
sliding his fingers over panels
smooth from eels and water,
pausing at the letterbox,
and he imagines again the dawn-
crowd leaving the party,
taking the door with them,
laughing as it fell from the bridge,
floated, then slowly sank.

Ghost Story

I will break into a tomb
in Highgate cemetery,
one that hasn't been opened
for a hundred years.
The bones in there won't mind.
I'll light a candle
and set up my camp bed,
then I'll read ghost stories
till the bones rattle
and come together
to form a skeleton.
I'll watch flesh form
on that skull again,
then the chest, the legs,
until a smiling old man
dressed in tweeds
sits down beside me
and asks me to read on.

All the Dogs

You should have seen him –
he stood in the park and whistled,
underneath an oak tree,
and all the dogs came bounding up
and sat around him,
keeping their big eyes on him,
tails going like pendulums.

And there was one cocker pup
who went and licked his hand,
and a labrador who whimpered
till the rest joined in.
Then he whistled a second time,
high-pitched as a stoat,
over all the shouted dog names
and whistles of owners,
till a flurry of paws
brought more dogs, panting,
as if they'd come miles,
and these too found space
on the flattened grass
to stare at the boy's
unmemorable face
which all the dogs found special.

The Field

Where the boy sees cattle
there was a battle
but the boy doesn't know it.
How could he know it?
He sees a field,
no sign of a shield
or an axe, or a sword,
not a cross word,
not a single shout,
just grass on the snout
of a bullock
as he stands on a rock,
chewing,
then mooing
till the boy walks on.
But when the sun
sinks in the sea
the boy would see,
instead of a farmer,
ghosts in armour
on ghost-horses.
He'd hear curses,
and the night-sky
miles high
would ring with steel
striking steel,
and the ghostly dead
and the odd head
would lie on the ground,
but not a sound
will the boy hear.

He won't be near.
He'll be home in bed,
as good as dead.

In the Desert

Wrapped in my camelhair rug
I'm camouflaged
out here in the desert.
My feet make no sound on the sand.
The sky is crawling with stars.

I shout, and it echoes
all the way to the sea.
No answering cry comes back to me.
I could be the last boy,
I could be up on the moon.

Nothing but flat for miles,
the occasional bone
strewn on the sand.
I take one back with me
to help bury my parachute.

I check my compass
and head due south-east.
A light wind covers my footprints.
I have no need of water.
I'll hit the oasis by dawn.

A Town Called Heaven

'One mile to Heaven'
said the signpost
and a voice from a speaker
said the same.
And in the distance
half-hidden by trees
he saw roofs and lampposts
and began to run.

'One mile to Heaven'
said the voice again.
One mile, he thought,
and slowed down.
He was in no hurry.
He liked trees.

He thought about 'Heaven'
as the name for a town.

Who'd called it that?
Who could live there?
What if they were bad?
Did people die there?
'One mile to Heaven'
said the voice again
but quieter, now
that the roofs had grown.

He shook his smiling head
on the street of Heaven.
He'd imagined free sweets
and model trains.
He found a town
much like his own
and posted a letter
to his Mum.

Note: In the Black Forest, in Germany, there is a town called Heaven.

What He Wanted

What did he want?
He wanted a UFO to land on the lawn
and a small grey man
to climb out and beckon to him,
then suddenly he'd be standing there,
without going down the stairs,
without opening the door,
and the little man wouldn't have to speak
but the boy would know what he thought
about the pollution of the seas,
about the use of guided missiles
to blow up half the world,
about famine and disease,
even about parents fighting,
and he'd ask the boy if he wanted
to come with them to their planet
but the boy would shake his head,
this was his planet.
He wanted to grow up on it
and become a politician,
change the way people lived,
make it a better place

for his own children,
one the little grey men could visit
openly, like him arriving in France,
and only then would he go
to visit their world in return.

A New Me

What's all this about a new me
to go with the new century?
I'm quite happy with the me I am.
So what if my room's a mess
and I watch all the TV I can!
I could be into cat-murders,
or running away to Paris,
or burning the school down.
I'd like a new you, and a new Dad,
a pair who wouldn't fight,
who'd treat me like a friend,
and who'd lose the no-gooders
who are always hanging around.
I'd like you to quit smoking,
and be mean to the bottle-bank.
I'd like Dad to join a gym,
but I keep all this to myself –
in fact, I'm quite prepared to
contemplate an amnesty
and let the two of you be
but only if the year 2000
makes you change your tune to me.

I Went to the Future

I went to the future,
stayed a week in a space hotel.
Met a boy who told me
no one ever got sick now
and all wars were gone.
He showed me a photo
of a family of dodos,
talked about his alien friend,
then suggested I join him
on a day-trip to the moon.

I went to the future,
stood there under a purple sun.
The buildings were silver
and no one walked the streets
in the icy wind.
I saw dead trees,
dogs that were half lion,
an artificial ozone layer.
It was the wrong future,
it wasn't mine.

I went to the future,
met the President of the Moon,
He asked if I wanted to live there,
said the air was clean.
He threw me a happiness ball.
I held it and smiled.
He struck up a tune

on the one-stringed zumbo
and I knew then I wanted to
follow him to the moon.

Sing

'Sing something!' roared the monk,
as he pulled the horse's reins
and brought the creature to a stop
outside the village sweet-shop
where children loitered in the rain.

'Sing something! Sing it now!
I've galloped here from France
through four nights and five days.
I started in a heat-haze.
Sing, and do a sun-dance!'

He sat there on his worn horse
and all the children stared,
then one young skinhead sang
a frantic scrap of rock-song
so loud the horse reared

and dumped the monk in mud.
But a smile broke on his beard.
He had his song, and the prance
of the horse was his sun-dance.
And sure enough, the sky cleared.

Up on the Roof

Up on the roof of a church
was a small, blond boy
and a black and white kitten.

Down below, the priest
was praying aloud,
pleading with God,

asking him to keep
this small boy from falling,
down from his church.

He couldn't phone the mother
as he didn't know her,
and cats all looked the same.

When the verger appeared
with a telescopic ladder
the priest closed his eyes

and, gripping his rosary,
he prayed in the dark until
the verger began to climb.

The boy was on his feet now
calling the kitten
who refused to move.

'Sit down,' begged the priest,
in an almost whisper
so as not to alarm the boy

who paid no attention,
walking over the slates
as if on the pavement

or as if he had wings –
with the sun in his hair
he looked like an angel.

When the verger's bald head
rose above the drainpipe
the boy had the kitten

and was walking back,
along the ridge,
with a beatific smile.

The Doctor's Son

'Look how the doctor's son
sits at the front of the church,
wears a tie every day.
Watch how he smiles
and greets the passers-by
in the mildest way.
Couldn't you think of *him*
instead of the rest of them
when you want to play?
Couldn't you learn
to be a bit like him,
and mind what you say?
I've heard he really swots
while you and your tramp-friends
waste the day.
He'll be a doctor too,
a surgeon perhaps,
while you and them stay
forever round here,
jobless, no doubt,
grown men at play.

Catch hold of yourself,
look at the doctor's boy
and lean that way.'

'I see the doctor's son
and I'd very much like
to chuck him into the sea.'

After Dinner

After the mad dinner party
when Mum ate nothing
and Dad ate everything,
saying it was his birthday,
and everyone drank a lot
(including my sister who's twelve –
she kept on helping herself),
so much that Mum and Dad fought,
till everyone went home,
leaving my sister to weep
while tired-out Mum fell asleep
and Dad sat there, glum –
after all this I invented
a language for bored boys,
something instead of toys,
to keep me and my kind contented
when people come to dine,
people who bypass us
unless we create a fuss
or they're too full with wine.
I call this language *Splat*
and only boys can learn it,
boys who've had to sit
through mad dinners like that.
I'll teach you a few words –
belush means bullshit,
stram means quit,
go home, wake the birds.
I'm not saying anymore

in case you're not boys.
I've had it with dinner noise.
Fhlorr means sore!

Me and Benjy

Me and Benjy, my teddybear,
went to bed to sleep.
What else would we do but sleep?
We couldn't, however –
the noise was atrocious,
shouting and laughing,
thumping and whooping –
Just imagine if that was us,
I whispered in Benjy's ear,
Guzzling wine and beer,
making one hell of a fuss!
What are we going to do?
I looked into Benjy's eyes,
Benjy's brownglass eyes.
Benjy, it has to be you,
I said, throwing him out,
then sliding out myself,
knocking a book from a shelf
with a thump, and a shout
from downstairs: *Go to sleep!*
The cheek of it, I thought.
One of their party ought

to investigate sleep-
possibilities up here,
to lie down on our bed,
pull the pillow over her head,
and ignore down there!
Come on Benjy, let's go.
We crept down the stairs,
me and that Benjybear,
and walked on tiptoe
to the living-room din
that vibrated the floor.
I pulled open the door
and chucked Benjy in.

My Party

Come to my party on Christmas Eve
in my rented air balloon.
Well, it's really a Zeppelin,
and at midnight you've got to leave.

Why? Because it's Christmas.
How do you get up there?
Hitch a ride on a helicopter.
Do it, and don't make a fuss,

and don't be late, or the angels
won't appear in their feathers
or their spacesuit evening wear,
and the food will go to the gulls.

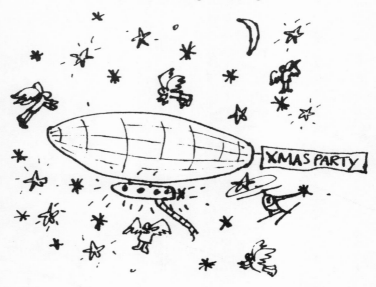

The food? There'll be larks' eggs
and flying fish, and roast crow.
(Horrible? How do you know?)
And specially imported moon figs.

Oh, and coke made with rain.
What about music? The stars
helped along by meteors
will cobble together a tune.

No more questions? Good.
Write it in the diary, then,
and spread the news to a friend
immediately. Is that understood?

Fatso in the Red Suit

It was October
and already the fake Santas
were filling the grottos
in the big stores,
and here was one on the telly
in a false white beard,
fat, like they always were,
his red-covered belly
bursting like he'd eaten a turkey
by himself, his voice
yo-ho-ho gruff,
his grin showing in each eye.
And Dave was on the sofa,
watching, with Dad beside him
sipping a glass of red wine
then choking on a guffaw
as he pointed at the screen,
'Would you look at him,
that Fatso in the Red Suit,'
and Dave turned green.

'Fatso in the Red Suit'
his Dad continued, singing it
to the beat of his foot,
'Fatso, Fatso in the Red Suit',
till Dave jumped up
and switched the telly off,
then turned to his Dad
and begged him to stop.
'He's not Fatso,' he shouted.
'He's Santa Claus.

You're almost as fat as he is.'
And Dave almost got clouted
but he carried on,
'He's not the real Santa
but he's still a bit of a Santa.
He's good, and you're mean,
and if you keep calling him
Fatso in the Red Suit,
he won't come here this year
and he'll do you harm.'

*

Over the next few weeks
Dave's Dad continued to sneer
at anything he'd see or hear
about Santa. And there were lots
of Fatsos in Red Suits about,
though Dave never called them that.
And each time his Dad did
Dave left the room. It happened
that Dad and Mum were fighting,
not about Fatsos in Red Suits,
about their own business. Every night
as Dave sat in bed reading
he'd hear them upstairs, shouting
at each other. Then one morning
Dad packed his bag and left
and Dave immediately blamed himself.

*

No word from Dad for days,
no luck ringing friends of his.

Mum moping in her room,
or saying he'd be back soon.

Dave watching things on telly
even he knew were silly.

Dave sad with no Dad,
thinking of the laughs they had,

wishing he knew where Dad was,
thinking: 'Dad, come home to us.'

Then, a message on the ansaphone –
Dad, for Dave, not Mum,

saying, 'Miss you more each day.'
To Dave he sounded far away.

*

Dave started to dream,
he dreamed five nights in a row,
then he stopped for two,
and dreamed five nights more.

He dreamed his Dad
was up in northern Iceland
working for a skinny man
who owned a toy factory.

Each of Dave's dreams
led into the next, like chapters
in a book, and in each
was Dave's Dad and the skinny man

who was also a stubbled man
and a grumpy man, and called
Dave's Dad Peter,
and didn't seem to like children.

Or that's how the first dream
showed it. And Dave's Dad
didn't like children either,
though Dave knew this was a lie.

In Dave's second dream
he heard the man being called
Mr Christmas, and saw
it wasn't children he disliked,

only naughty children,
of which there were plenty, he said,
and Dave's Dad had the job
of haunting the dreams of these.

Dave woke up at this,
but he didn't feel haunted.
His Dad wasn't in his dreams
nearly enough, but Mr Christmas was.

On the third night
Dave dreamed the painted sign
above the factory door –
it said *Sinte Klass*.

And he began to notice
the changing look of Mr Christmas,

his beard was thick now
though he was still skinny.

And each night his clothes
were different, from jeans
to a bishop's suit. And now
Dave's Dad called him Nick.

Dave's two dreamless nights
were needed for resting,
but he did a lot of thinking
and almost told his Mum.

The sixth dream was in colour
and Mr Christmas was in green,
while Dave's Dad was in black
as both peered into a book.

The dream went in close-up.
It was a notebook, with lists
of the naughty children
and Dave saw his name there.

Mr Christmas was drinking beer
in dream seven, and Dad
was handing him a cigar,
and they'd both put on weight.

And Mr Christmas would change clothes
in mid-dream, from blue
to brown, to any colour, as if
he was looking for the right colour.

And the toys kept mounting
at the back of the factory,
each with a tab that matched
a name in a second notebook.

Dave couldn't read these
and the last dreams didn't help –
they were jumbled, and strange
and all took place on Christmas Eve,

(still weeks away) when bees
hummed psalms at midnight,
and animals could talk
and angels sang in pine trees,

and Mr Christmas rode among them
on a white horse, pulling a cart
full of toys, his beard white now
and him fat and wearing red.

*

When the dreams stopped
Dave wrote a letter,

he addressed it 'Mr Christmas',
made a photocopy,
sent one to Greenland,
the other to Iceland.

He wrote 'Dear Mr Christmas,
I don't want any toys,
I want my Dad –
the man you call Peter
who dresses in black.
I want him back.'

*

It was mid-December
when Dave got a letter
from his Dad,
from the north of England,
enclosing a photo
of him in a grotto
in a red suit
and falsely fat.

He said to tell Mum
he'd be home
for Christmas,
and he'd bring lots –
a turkey
and brandy
and as many toys
as he'd fit on the bus.

And on Christmas Eve
as they made to leave

for church
he stood on the porch
in his red suit
looking *really* fat —
Dave's Dad was home
and Santa had still to come.

Home

When I think of home I see
a white pebbledashed house
sharing a yard with an ex-dancehall
where Le Mans is taking place
with a pedal-jeep and tricycles, and
high on a wooden beam a boy sits,
a stopwatch in his hands;
and through a starred window comes
the fatigued sound of a tractor
stealing sand from the ocean
leaving a yellow trail on tar,
a choir of dog-yelps in the air.

The House

The house had a dozen bedrooms,
each of them cold, and the wind
battered the windows and blew down
power-lines to leave the house dark.
Rats lived in the foundations,
sending scouts under the stairs
for a year or two, and once
a friendly ghost was glimpsed
at the foot of a bed. Downhill
half a mile was the Atlantic,
with its ration of the drowned –
one of whom visited the house,
carried there on a door.
It hosted dry corpses, too,
with nostrils huge to a child,
but never a murder –
except the lambs bled dry
in the yard outside. Sunlight
never took over the interior,
and after dark the cockroaches
came from under a cupboard
to be eaten by the dog.
Crows were always sitting
on the wires, planning nests
in the chimneys, and a shotgun
sometimes blew a few away.
Neighbours never entered
as often as in other houses,
but it did have a piano upstairs.
And I did grow up there.

TWO

Lucy's Gosling

Lucy calls her gosling Mona
and takes her for walks by the sea.
There is such a wet lot of sea
all around Lucy, all around.

You got it, she lives on an island,
an island named Glashedy.

Out there the ships criss-cross
and never come near.
Lucy wouldn't want them near,
nor would Mona.

It's crowded enough on the island,
the island named Glashedy.

There's Dad, when he's not fishing.
There's Mona and Lucy.
There's Mona and Lucy.
Oh, and there's Grandpa in the cave.

Yes, there's a cave on the island,
the island named Glashedy.

I bet you like going in caves.
This one's where Lucy sleeps,
where Mona, Dad and Grandpa sleep
in the quiet and the sea air.

Imagine, no traffic on the island,
the island named Glashedy.

Lucy's Grandpa eyes her gosling.
Says he's fed up with fish,
nothing to eat but fish.
Lucy tells him 'Eat yourself.'

A gosling is quite safe on the island,
the island named Glashedy.

OK, a girl with a gosling,
but won't the gosling grow?
So what? Lucy will grow
into a big girl with a goose.

And they'll grow old on the island,
the island named Glashedy.

Cows on the Beach

Two cows,
fed-up with grass, field, farmer,
barged through barbed wire
and found the beach.
Each mooed to each:
This is a better place to be,
a stretch of sand next to the sea,
this is the place for me.
And they stayed there all day,
strayed this way, that way,
over to rocks,
past discarded socks,
ignoring the few people they met
(it wasn't high season yet).
They dipped hooves in the sea,
got wet up to the knee,
they swallowed pebbles and sand,
found them a bit bland,
washed them down with sea-water,
decided they really ought to
rest for an hour.
Both were sure
they'd never leave here.
Imagine, they'd lived so near
and never knew!
With a swapped moo
they sank into sleep,
woke to the yellow jeep
of the farmer
revving there
feet from the incoming sea.

This is no place for cows to be,
he shouted, and slapped them
with seaweed, all the way home.

Fishbones Dreaming

Fishbones lay in the smelly bin.
He was a head, a backbone and a tail.
Soon the cats would be in for him.

He didn't like to be this way.
He shut his eyes and dreamed back.

Back to when he was fat, and hot on a plate.
Beside green beans, with lemon juice
squeezed on him. And a man with a knife
and fork raised, about to eat him.

He didn't like to be this way.
He shut his eyes and dreamed back.

Back to when he was frozen in the freezer.
With lamb cutlets and minced beef and prawns.
Three months he was in there.

He didn't like to be this way.
He shut his eyes and dreamed back.

Back to when he was squirming in a net,
with thousands of other fish, on the deck
of a boat. And the rain falling
wasn't wet enough to breathe in.

He didn't like to be this way.
He shut his eyes and dreamed back.

Back to when he was darting through the sea,
past crabs and jellyfish, and others
like himself. Or surfacing to jump for flies
and feel the sun on his face.

He liked to be this way.
He dreamed hard to try and stay there.

Worrying Days

By now the donkey knew
he was safe from the stew.
He was old,
he was easily cold.
He had a wonky heart,
he could hardly pull the olive cart,
but at least he wouldn't fill
the casserole
all winter.
Worrying days were over.

And on the shore road
with a light load
of driftwood
he felt he could
gallop across Sicily
immediately.
Wild garlic was in the air
when his owner stopped to stare
at his rump, and shout 'Salami!' –
whatever that meant. 'Salami!'

The White Bear and the Arctic Fox

A white bear and an arctic fox
hid in a cave in the snow.
Men with guns were out there.
They wished they'd go.

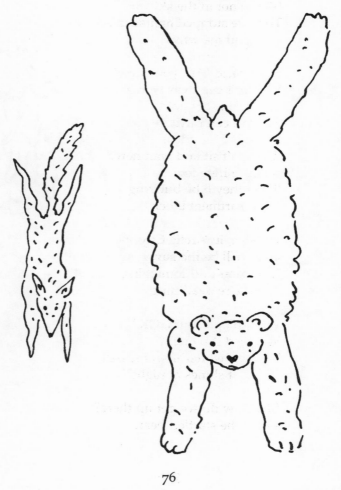

Bear looked at fox and said
'I wish we weren't white.
That's why they want us.
    We shine at night.'

Fox sneered and shook his tail.
'We're not in the sky.'
Then he stopped and said
    'Tell me why.'

Bear asked 'Are you crazy?
We can't get away.
This is our habitat.
    We can't fly.'

'We can't sit and wait here.'
said the irate fox.
'Soon they'll be building
    apartment blocks

with ice, in Arctic City,
and we'll be the rugs.
If we don't do something
    we're dead mugs.

We can't go south, OK?
We need it white.
Where's whiter than the ball
    that shines at night?'

'But how do we get up there?'
asked the startled bear.

'And if we managed it
    would we have air?'

As they argued like this
the hunters found them
and before they could run
    they shot them.

The Flying Spring Onion

The flying spring onion
   flew through the air
      over to where
the tomatoes grew in rows
   and he said to those
      seed-filled creatures
My rooted days are done,
   so while you sit here
      sucking sun
I'll be away and gone,
   to Greenland
      where they eat no green
      and I won't be seen
in a salad bowl with you,
   stung by lemon,
      greased by oil,
and nothing at all to do
   except wait to be eaten.
With that he twirled
   his green propellers
and rose above the rows
   of red balls
who stared as he grew small
   and disappeared.

Cecil, the Spider

Cecil, the spider,
belongs to a boy
called Tom.
He lives at the top
of the coldwater tap
on the bath.
It's dry up there,
even when water
spurts out.
No room for a web –
Cecil doesn't care
a whit.
Tom feeds him
bits of hard skin
and toenails.
Cecil runs out
the tap's long spout
and drops
onto the bubbly
water's surface
and walks.
I bet you didn't know
spiders could walk
on water.
Or that they ate
bits of our skin
and toenails.
Or that a pipe
connects the taps
in England.
So if Cecil escapes

it might be you
he'll walk to
out of the steam,
eyeing the soles
of your feet.

Grandpa's Monkeys

My maternal Grandpa was a sailor
    who, back in the 1920s,
    took an unnatural fancy
to that sheer rock called Gibraltar.

The women there were half-Spanish,
    had black eyes, wore little,
    but Grandpa couldn't settle
with any female, except the ape-ish

ones who hung from the rock's face
    with one hand, and squealed
    at any ship that wheeled
into the Straits at an iceberg's pace.

And he brought one home, did Gramps,
    to our gawping Cardiff street,
    with black shoes on its feet,
and they both died of the same mumps.

Mr Bluejack

Mr Bluejack likes the freezer,
sticks his head in when it's hot.
One son wants to do it also,
the other does not.

Mr Bluejack keeps a budgie,
calls it Greenface, sets it free.
One son wants it in the freezer,
the other won't agree.

Mr Bluejack's budgie, Greenface,
flies onto the frying pan.
One son can't imagine frying,
the other can.

Mr Bluejack lets his budgie
perch upon the chandelier.
One son loves its tuneless singing,
the other can't hear.

Mr Bluejack calls the freezer
Joe, and strokes its shiny door.
One son likes it less each day,
the other more.

Mr Bluejack wants his sons
to rear budgies of their own.
One son answers with a whoop,
the other with a moan.

Mr Bluejack stuffs the budgie
and both sons inside Joe.
One son pleads for Dad to join them,
the other whispers 'No!'

Captain Hately

In that big house
  at the top of the drive,
    behind a locked door
Captain Hately prowls the top floor,
carrying a candle
  or a paraffin lamp
    from room to room,
leaning forward, peering through the gloom,
always listening
  for a key in the lock,
    the sound of a car,
always waiting, wondering where they are,
those four sons
  he raised alone,
    all gone away
and seldom, if ever, coming back to stay,
despite the gifts
  he's promised them
    with his own breath,
gifts they'll get in time, after his death –
for one, the island,
  one, the estate,
    another, his wealth,
for the fourth, his favourite, the house itself
with his grave ready
  by the chestnut tree
    on the front lawn.
And years of Captain Hately prowling on.

Man on the Line

When the toothbrush hit the teeth
      the phone rang.
It was early, but not too early.
Oh, let's be honest, it was late!

'Are you quite awake?' a voice said,
      a man's voice.
'I, myself, have finished lunch,
I was chewing while you were snoring.'

She held the receiver away from her,
      she stared at it
and went to put it gently down.
'Don't hang up on me,' he shouted,

this man on the end of the line.
      Who was he?
'It doesn't matter who I am,
I've a bone to pick with you.

'What do you think you're doing
      sleeping late?
Think of what you missed this morning,
think of all you could have done.

'I, myself, don't sleep now.
      I gave it up.
Know what I call a night's sleep?
Another little slice of death.

'I know *you* need some sleep.
                    Most do.
But don't overdo it, don't be greedy,
jump up early, get out there.'

The man on the line hung up.
                    She did too
and tiptoed down the stairs to bed
to rest, to clear her ringing head.

The Silent Knight

He went into a huff at Christmas,
there in the crowded church
with the choir behind him, singing hymns
about kings, and mangers
and a holy, silent *night*!

So he became a silent *knight*,
and stormed from the church
to don his armour, mount his horse
and head for his castle home
where he brooded in the bedroom

then pinned up a notice
sacking all the servants,
advertising for dumb replacements,
and warning his wife
never to speak to him again.

And each month at the joust
he was invincible,
his lance became a tin-opener
leaving the meat of knights
for maggots to gobble,

while he never boasted
or cried out in triumph,
just galloped home to his silent castle
where harpists were barred
and monks went on the fire.

The Nobody on the Hill

No one knows he lives there,
not even the postman
as nobody writes.
His family, if he had any,
are dead, and years before
they thought him dead
for certain. They'd laugh
if they saw him on this hill.

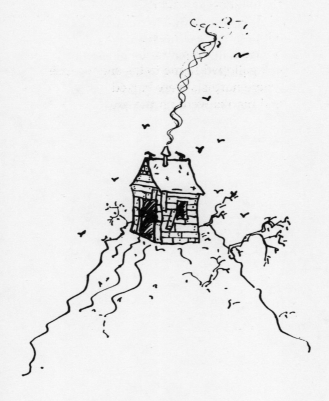

They'd stand before his hut
and shake their heads.
Home in the city
they had a grand house,
and he lived there once.
An avenue of trees
instead of this hill.
Even their ghosts avoid it.

Beyond the hill is a bog
and beyond that, nothing –
this suits him. He hunted
long and far for the site.
He hammered together the hut
in two days. He never leaves
the hill. He'll die there
and no one will find him.

The Not So Slow Loris

The slow loris
           objected
                    to her name!
Well, she liked *loris* but not *slow*.
She was a primate too!
                    Who was man
to bandy names about?
                    What did he know,
sun-lover, long pig!
                    Let him stick
to cockroaches and kangaroos.
He didn't say *slow tortoise*.
                    He made her sick!

The slow loris
           sat on a grave
                    and fumed!

She paid no attention to the moon
or the stupid stars –
                    man's stuff!
She wanted to go
                into Rangoon
and complain.
                She wanted man
to change the dictionaries.
She wanted apologies.
                She had no plan.

White Dog with Four Black Spots

The white dog with four black spots
is barking up the beach.
He is barking at water-skiers
and at dead baby crabs.
He tears along the sand, this way and that.
He runs into the sea, asking
'Where are the waves today?'
He barks at the stubborn sky
that keeps the sun hidden.
Most of all he barks at the children
for running away from him,
for carrying buckets of sand,
for splashing in the water.

One of the white dog's four black spots
covers his left eye. Maybe that's why
the sand-brown dog is circling
without being noticed.

There are no spots on this dog.
No sounds come from him.
He has no eyes for the sea, the sky
or the children, only the white dog
and the black spots. He wants to
bite the spots off, one by one.
He wants to bite some white off
for spots of his own. He *wants* to.

Bones

The horse fell in the harbour,
was splashing in the water
with the cart strapped to his back.
And a cyclist with sunglasses
and a woman with a pram
kept on going – but not the man
with the mongrel in a sack.
He dropped all and dived straight in.

The horse kept neighing
while the man was saving him
and the dog was chewing free.
Maybe the horse knew
that the man was on his way
to drown the dog. Maybe the dog
had barked this to the horse.
Oh, there were bones in the cart.

Dog in Space

The barking in space
has died out now,
though dogbones rattle.
And the marks of teeth
on the sputnik's hull
are proof of a battle
impossible to win.

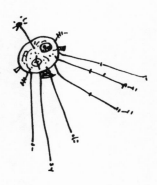

And asteroid-dents
were no help at all.
Did the dog see,
through the window,
earth's blue ball?
Did the dog know
that no other dog
had made that circle
around the earth –
her historic spin
that turned eternal?

The Small Skeleton and the Big One

Beneath one skeleton was another skeleton,
and this one was smaller. And a crab
had a good home in its pelvis.

The small skeleton dreamed of swinging,
the big skeleton of walking.

The big one remembered the shark
that ate the small one and stayed hungry.
The small one remembered nuts,

and dreamed, dreamed hard of branches.
The big one dreamed of dances.

It heard again the ship's siren,
and saw the lifeboats being lowered.
The small skeleton smelled fire.

It dreamed of ropes and rooftops.
The big one dreamed of chips

or that last meal of deep-fried scampi
before he fed the shark.
The small one remembered his cage,

and dreamed of the still-locked door,
while the big one dreamed of armchairs

and the small skeleton and the big one
with flesh again, monkey and human.

Flat Bird

Forced off the pavement
by my own hurry
and three women walking abreast,
I spy a blob on the tarmac
like a map of a country
or a pattern in cement,
and as I step over it
I really look at it,
till I see what it is –
I don't want to believe it
but it's a flat bird,
a totally flat bird.

It's hard to make out
what kind of bird.
It's hard to imagine it airborne,
or having a third dimension,
or ever being heard.
Did that driver shout,

who crushed the skull,
and left the bird dead
for other drivers to flatten?
How long did it take to happen,
to make a flat bird,
a totally flat bird?

While I Practise My Piano

I'm being haunted by child spirits.
The door keeps opening.
Will you sit in the room with me
while I practise my piano?
You can even sing –
they won't like that,
your voice would send a bee
careering into a wall,
or would start a cat wailing.
There's the door again,
why are you so slow
at getting in here?
I've got to keep playing –
else the child spirits
will take over my piano
and play tunes of their own,
tunes that might scare me,

and once they got going
they'd never stop, so
please keep me company,
please sit in the room with me
while I practise my piano.

Smile

Smile, go on, smile!
Anyone would think, to look at you,
that your cat was on the barbecue
or your best friend had died.
Go on, curve your mouth.
Take a look at that beggar,
or that one-legged bus conductor.
Where's *your* cross?
Smile, slap your thigh.
Hiccup, make a horse noise,
lollop through the house,
fizz up your coffee.
Take down your guitar
from its air-shelf and play
imaginary reggae
out through the open door.
And smile, remember, smile,
give those teeth some sun,
grin at everyone,
do it now, go on, SMILE!

Spotlight

Switch the spotlights on.
Make them mainly white
but have at least one red or blue.
Turn one light on each of you,
and when you're lit,
break out, have some fun –
dance, one-legged, till you sweat,
shake, collapsing in a pool,
sing a quaky, wordless song,
pretend to be a vulture,
act the ancient high-bred fool,
lie down, clap your feet,
mime a waking panther,
or a dog that's just been stung –
or any act that takes your fancy
in that round of light.
Don't stand back and crush the wall.
Don't put up a fight.
We need some wild applause,
but first we need SPOTLIGHT!

The Bad Girl Haiku

Flat

She pushed the big stone
over the gate, down on top
of her pet tortoise.

Experiment

She killed the rabbit
then chucked it in the pond to
see if it would float.

Big Sister

She pegged the baby
to the clothesline, then laughed at
his panicky cries.

Censor

She binned the letters
her Mum was keeping hidden
in a sock drawer.

Chopsticks

She poked the white rat
in the eyes with the chopsticks
her Dad always used.

The Butcher

After his parrot escaped
the butcher stood at the door
shouting into the sky.

'Come back, parrot,' he roared
while a queue waited
for lambchops and beef,
sausages, burgers and chicken –

they could take what they liked
for all the butcher cared,
but they'd better be quick.

He got his matches out
and set fire to the shop,
then went to the airport
to fly to Venezuela

where he hired a raft
and set off down the Orinoco
with three Indian guides

who led him into a swamp
and robbed him, then killed him,
and his bones are still there
while the parrot is free.

The Burglar

When the burglar went out
to burgle a house

When the burglar pulled on
his black polo-neck,
his beret, his Reeboks

When the burglar rattled
his skeleton keys,
checked he had his street-map,
said goodbye to his budgie

When the burglar shouldered
an empty bag, big enough
to take as much swag
as the burglar could carry

When the burglar waited
for the bus

When the burglar stood
at the bottom of the street
where the house he'd picked
to burgle was

When the burglar burgled
he didn't know
that another burglar
was inside *his* house

And only the budgie would see

God of Smell

I am the God of Smell,
my name is Pongo.
I live in the sewers of Calcutta
and nobody worships me
like they worship those other gods.
None of them can fill the wind
with the stench of corpses
after an earthquake,
none of them make feet sweat.
I loathe deodorants
and all brands of perfume,
although flowers are OK
for the days I feel benign
towards the world of humans –
rare days, though, rare . . .
I have 500 skunk guards
and a giant's nose I cut off
that can still smell danger –
soap machines and detergents,
blasts of clean fresh air,
floods of pure spring water,
all sent to clean the sewers
and flush me out to sea,
but it wouldn't work, anyway,
I'd pollute the water,
make it stink, make fish taste bad,
so I'm better left where I am.
Put up with my whiff, then,
and remember, it could be stronger.
It will be, one day.

Goddess of Ice

I am the Goddess of Ice,
my name is Po Lar.
I live on the surface of Pluto
where none of you will ever get to
but I come to you frequently –
I go from continent to continent
depending on the season
but I never touch Africa.
I have a home in the Arctic
and another in the Antarctic,
both guarded by polar bears.
Water is my slave.
I hate the sun
but one day he'll burn out
and I'll set my ice on the world.

Goddess of Poison

I am the Goddess of Poison,
my name is Lethaldrop.
I'm very compatible with water,
whisky even more so –
I lurk there, undetected,
until the autopsy.
Hah! bullets are so unsubtle
and disease is too slow.
I'm found in plants everywhere
though my favourite haunts
are the prettiest mushrooms.
A constant strain of humans
are my footsoldiers –
they poison their partners,
this is especially true of women
and I'm proud of them
(even when it's food-poisoning
and unintentional). My pets
are snakes, spiders and scorpions
and a whole host of viruses
that soon will wipe you out,
and I'll rule over a planet
as dead as the moon.

God of Rain

I am the God of Rain,
my name is Drencher.
I am first cousin of the sea.
My favourite countries are these –
Ireland all the year round,
India during the monsoon.
I never go near the Sahara.
I hate umbrella-factories
and raincoat manufacturers.
I'm on good terms with illnesses
like the cold, or pneumonia,
and sometimes I set up flooding
which leads to drowning,
but before you begin to curse me
let me ask you this –
who feeds the streams
and gives you drinking water?
And what about the trees,
the flowers, the fish in the sea?
Still not convinced?
Go, then, and live on Mars!

Resurrected

If I got out of my grave
in a hundred years' time
I'd ignore the other risen dead
sniffing flowers, brushing their clothes,
fixing their hair, feeling their faces –
I wouldn't even read my epitaph,
but I'd make for the river
and I'd jump in, with all my clothes on,
and I'd swim, stiffly, till I was clean,
then I'd climb on the boat
waiting to take us to town.

I'd speak to nobody,
as I'd have lost the habit,
and the language would have grown.
The later dead would stare at me,
at my once-again-trendy clothes,
and of course I'd be young again
with half an eye for the women,
but first I'd head for a bar
for a long-postponed beer, and I'd
ask where a Thai restaurant was,
shining my antique coins.

Getting Rid of the Box

The box had five locks
and four false floors,
and a welded-shut door.

And six men carried it
to a nuclear submarine
which burrowed through the ocean

to the first icy suburb
of Antarctica, where no
human marked the ice or snow.

The captain gave the order
to unleash a torpedo
as deep in the ice as it would go,

then in the blast hole
he offloaded the box
and covered it with ice-rocks,

then a second torpedo
brought more ice collapsing
onto the nauseous thing,

and at last he knew
the box's grisly cargo
was as safe as the snow,

and none of that stuff
we'd all crammed in
would ever bother us again.

The Moon

The moon is a ball of ghosts,
    she said,
and three astronauts know
but they ain't telling. Why?
Because the ghosts insisted,
    she said,
and made the astronauts go.

For their own good, of course,
    she said
in a whispery tone of voice,
and three ghosts came with them
to Earth, then to three homes,
    she said.
The astronauts had no choice.

All three heads are grey,
    she said,
and it's no wonder. And none
is an astronaut any longer
but all three know for sure,
    she said,
they'll be back on the moon.

The Money Tree

Listen, there *is* a money tree.
I know you don't believe me,
and I didn't when Bill told me
that his mate Joe's brother
waters it every day.

It's not just water – there's sweat
and blood mixed in, not so's
you'd notice, Joe's brother says,
and he should know because
he mixes it himself.

There's another works with him,
another money-gardener

and they hate each other,
watch each other like dogs –
that's part of the job.

The tree is in a courtyard
surrounded by blank walls
with slits for rifles,
and a ceiling of perspex
that can slide open.

Where is this courtyard?
Joe's brother doesn't know.
Every morning he has to go
to a rooftop in the city
where a copter lands.

They put on a blindfold
and no-one speaks. They whirr
Joe's brother somewhere
in the city, he can't say.
It's best he can't.

Why is there only one tree?
That's what I want to know.
You'd think they'd grow
plantations of the stuff.
Joe's brother laughs.

He sees the look
on the faces that come
every weekday at noon
to collect the picked leaves.
They wouldn't share.

If you still don't believe me
come here and we'll go
see Bill, and then Joe
and then his brother,
and ask him yourself.

Gold

The gold bars lie buried in the silt
and three skeletons lie guarding them,
three males, though the squid who sleeps
in the first skull couldn't say
and couldn't care less. To her
it is a cave, a domed cavern
she shares with no one. And who
could expect her to guess the plans
that had pulsed there, stalled,
till the ship reached Spain – expect her
to dream the face of the new wife
whose image had lodged there,
the image that faded with death?
The second skull lies yards away
from its long bones, and this one
is empty. But this one, too,

127

had taken in Spanish and spoken it out,
and had often eyed the gold.
Its eye-holes stare there still.
A crab sits in the third skull,
watching – a spider gone hard.
He is dictator of this stretch
of water, and the fact that he sits
in the skull of a Captain
is as useless to him as gold.
And nowhere on the skull wall
is a wisp of the knowledge
that the Captain's villa is ruined.
And the gold bars were going there
unknown to the crew. And unknown
to the divers whose boat churns above –
all they know is there's gold here.